PICTURE PUZZLER

A NATURAL HISTORY HIDE-AND-SEEK

illustrated by

KSENIA BAKHAREVA

written by

RACHEL WILLIAMS

MAGIC CAT  PUBLISHING

CONTENTS

STEP INTO THESE
REAL-WORLD HABITATS...

STEP INTO A HIDDEN WORLD...

Life in the wild is adventurous – and full of danger. From the driest desert to the tallest mountain, animals big and small have learned to stay hidden from prey and predators, finding ways to eat . . . and not be eaten!

CAMOUFLAGE, which was originally a French word, is a skill creatures use to disguise themselves. All of the animals in this book have adapted to their habitats in the most inventive ways.

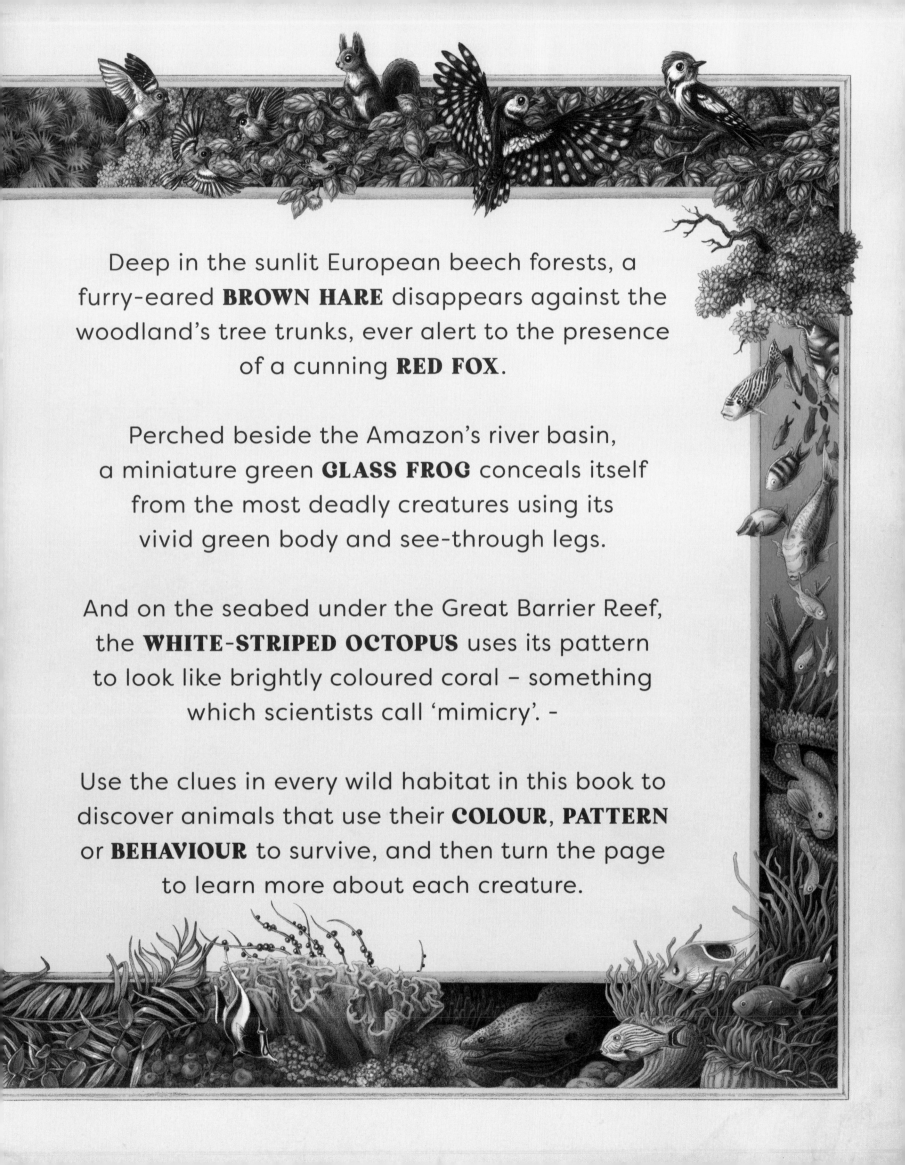

Deep in the sunlit European beech forests, a furry-eared **BROWN HARE** disappears against the woodland's tree trunks, ever alert to the presence of a cunning **RED FOX**.

Perched beside the Amazon's river basin, a miniature green **GLASS FROG** conceals itself from the most deadly creatures using its vivid green body and see-through legs.

And on the seabed under the Great Barrier Reef, the **WHITE-STRIPED OCTOPUS** uses its pattern to look like brightly coloured coral – something which scientists call 'mimicry'. -

Use the clues in every wild habitat in this book to discover animals that use their **COLOUR**, **PATTERN** or **BEHAVIOUR** to survive, and then turn the page to learn more about each creature.

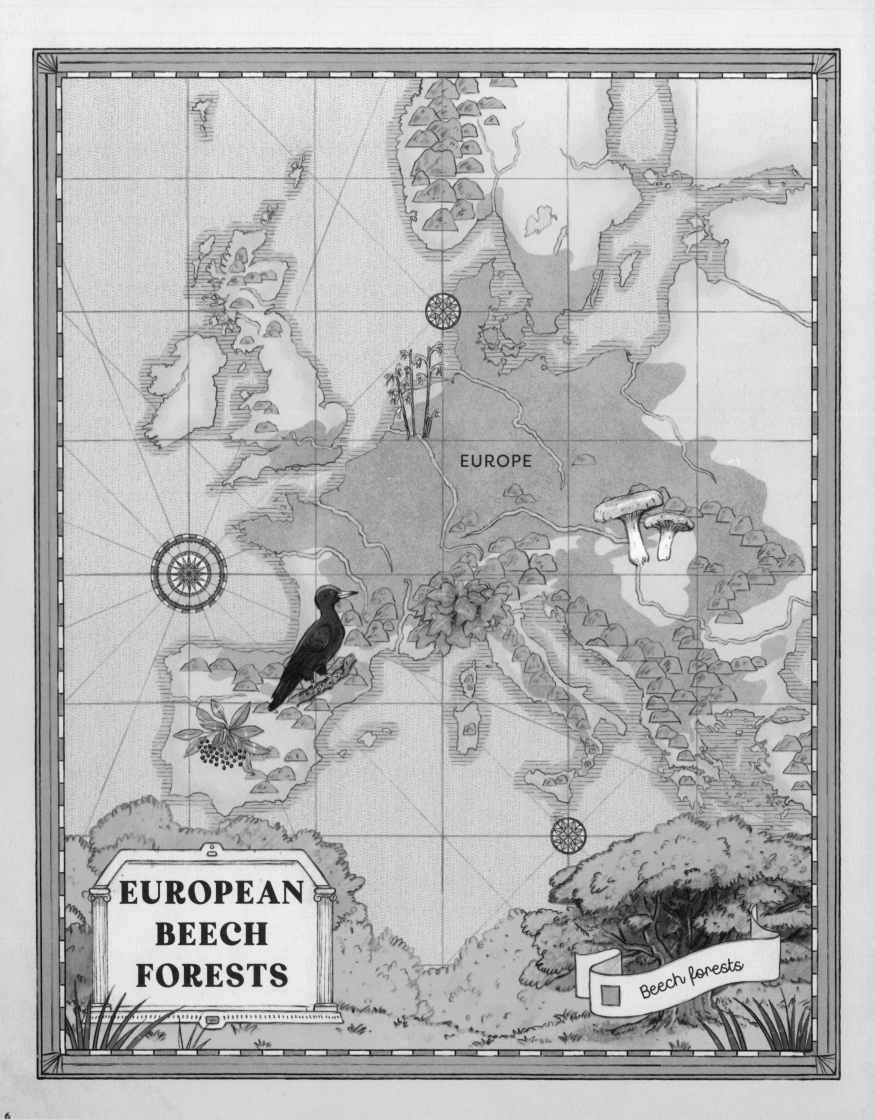

EUROPE

EUROPEAN BEECH FORESTS

Beech forests

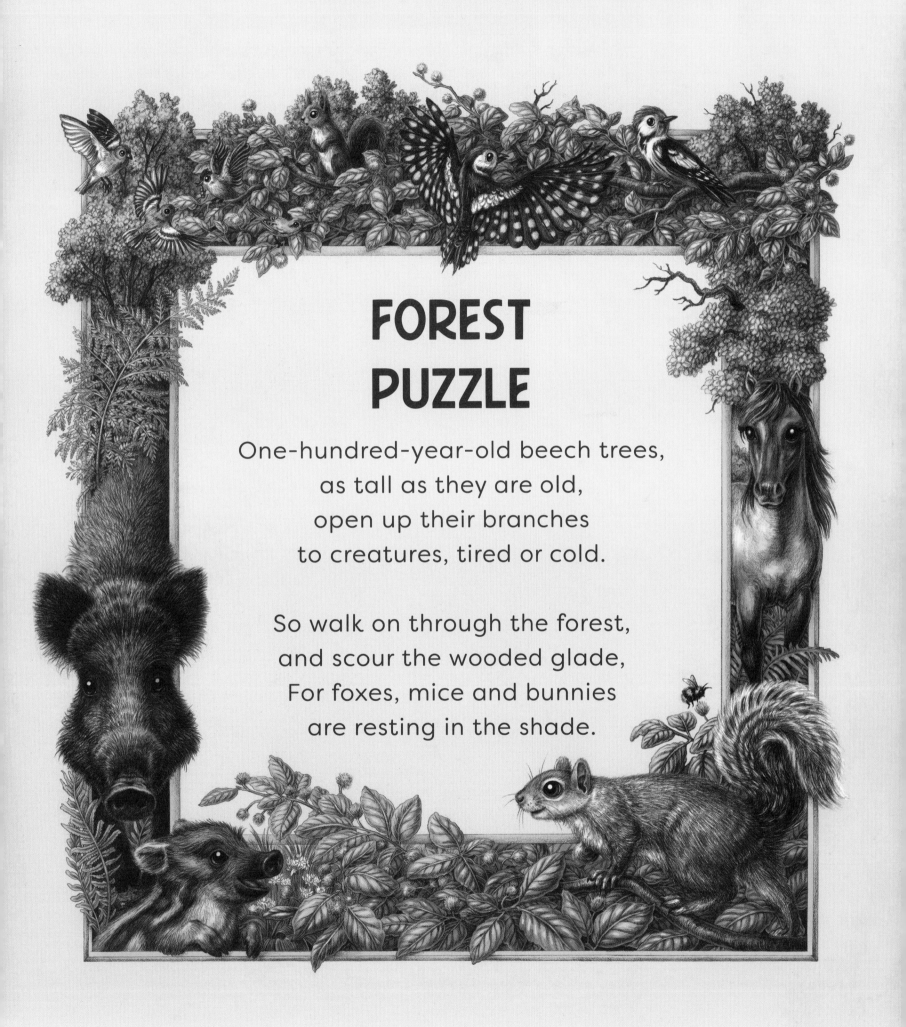

FOREST PUZZLE

One-hundred-year-old beech trees,
as tall as they are old,
open up their branches
to creatures, tired or cold.

So walk on through the forest,
and scour the wooded glade,
For foxes, mice and bunnies
are resting in the shade.

CAN YOU FIND
these bold, bright creatures?

A wild pony that's gentle and tame, see my dark tail and long, black mane. I'm a... **KONIK PONY**

Dappled shade is where I hide, my spotted coat's a great disguise. I'm a... **FALLOW DEER**

I slither into sunny spots and later hide by leaves or rocks. I'm an... **ADDER**

My stripy face is black and white, which helps me stay well out of sight. I'm a... **BADGER**

I peck peck peck upon a tree, to let you know my territory. I'm a... **MIDDLE SPOTTED WOODPECKER**

My big snout helps me root around for tasty acorns on the ground. I'm a... **WILD BOAR**

My feathers make me hard to spy, but a bright red line sits above each eye. I'm a...**WESTERN CAPERCAILLIE**

I like to munch on fruits and seeds, you'll find me climbing in a tree. I'm a... **EUROPEAN DORMOUSE**

My back legs make me a fast sprinter, I shelter in the woods in winter. I'm a... **BROWN HARE**

They say that I'm a cunning creature, my orange coat is my best feature. I'm a... **RED FOX**

I'm by the water – a slippery fellow – see my markings of black and yellow. I'm a... **FIRE SALAMANDER**

Large eyes give me excellent sight, you'll find me hunting through the night. I'm an... **EAGLE OWL**

Notes on... EUROPEAN BEECH FORESTS

HUNDREDS OF YEARS AGO, MUCH OF EUROPE WAS COVERED BY ENORMOUS BEECH TREE FORESTS.

Many of these forests still exist, and their ancient trees are more than a century old. Featuring the world's largest and tallest trees, can be found in eighteen different countries.

Many of the animal species living in these these forests are as old as the trees.

DID YOU SPOT ALL OF THE MASTERS OF DISGUISE?

Turn back a page to see if you can find the creatures below, whose camouflage makes them nearly impossible to find.

I have tufts of feathers on my head that look like ears!

EAGLE OWL
Bubo bubo

Eagle owls are excellent hunters. They have hooked beaks, powerful feet which they use to snatch their prey; and great vision, which helps them to see in the dark.

My mottled feathers keep me hidden against the tree bark.

My black and yellow markings warn hungry predators to stay away!

Salamander larva

FIRE SALAMANDER
Salamandra salamandra

The fire salamander is an amphibian, which meansit lives on land and spends much of its life near water. Females carry their young as eggs inside their body and give birth to salamander larvae in a pond or river.

It's dark and damp here under the cool, wet grass near the river. . . that's just how I like it.

RED FOX
Vulpes vulpes

Red fox homes — called dens — are usually on the edges of forests, near fields where there is plenty of prey for them to hunt.

My paw pads are furry, which muffles the sound of my steps in the forest.

A rusty, red coat helps me stay hidden from view.

BROWN HARE
Lepus europaeus

Unlike rabbits, brown hares do not dig burrows. Instead, they shelter in small dips in the ground known as 'forms'.

My long ears help me listen for predators

Did you see me hiding in the tall grass behind the pony?

EUROPEAN DORMOUSE
Glis glis

This mouse looks a bit like a squirrel, and its long, bushy tail helps it to balance in trees.

WESTERN CAPERCAILLIE
Tetrao urogallus

Female western capercaillie is smaller than the colourful male, and her plumage keeps her well hidden.

I can cling to mossy tree branches with my large feet and sharp claws.

I have feathered legs for protection against the cold.

Turn to page 42 to find all the animals from the beech forest

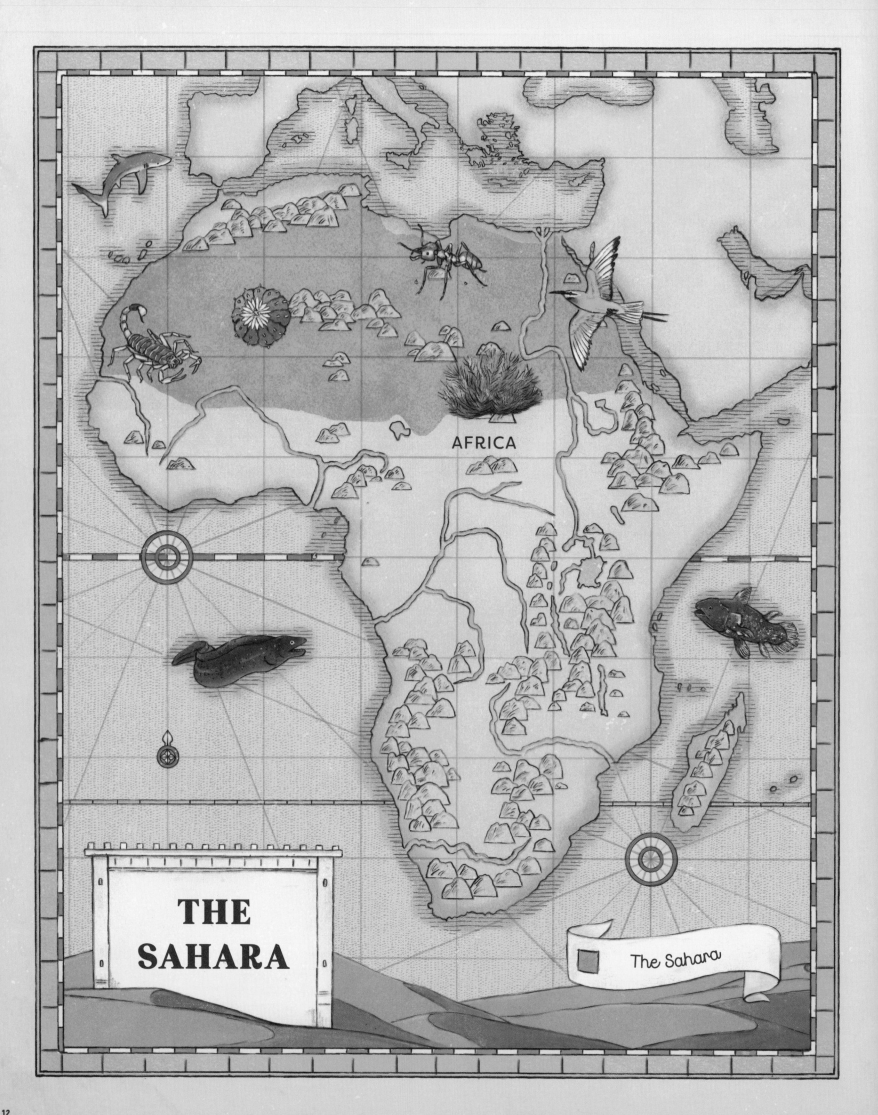

AFRICA

THE
SAHARA

The Sahara

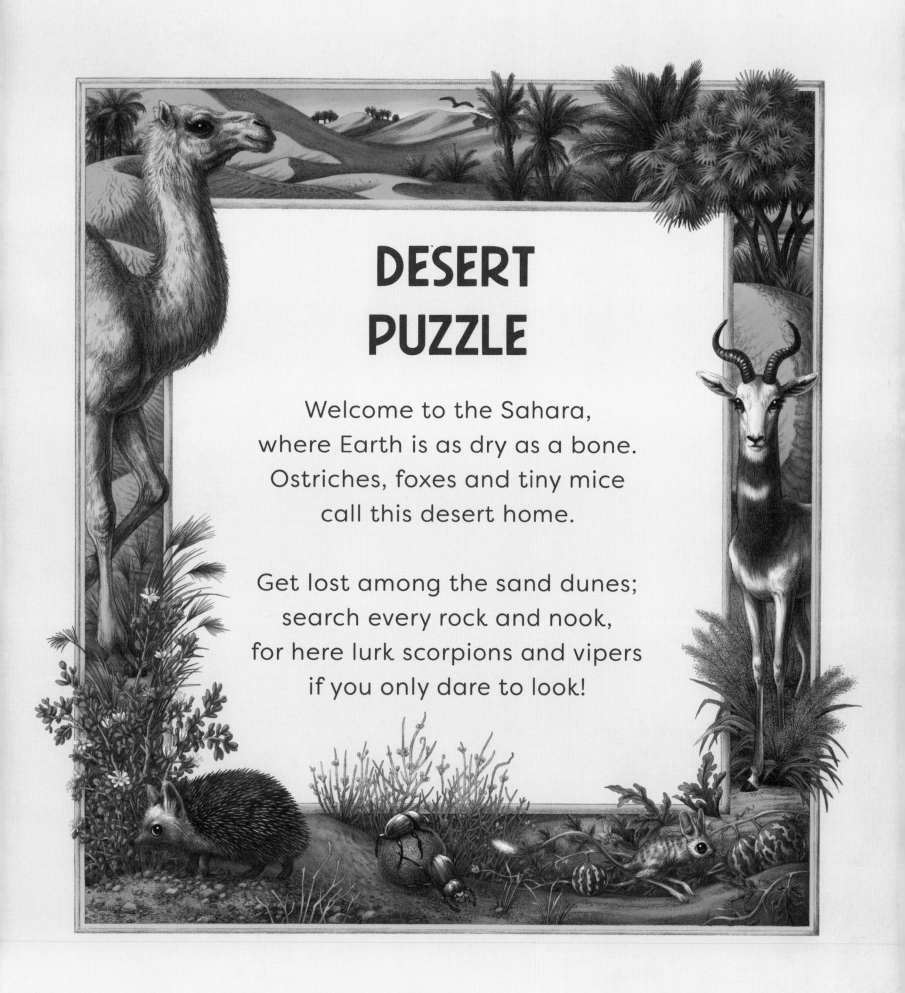

DESERT PUZZLE

Welcome to the Sahara,
where Earth is as dry as a bone.
Ostriches, foxes and tiny mice
call this desert home.

Get lost among the sand dunes;
search every rock and nook,
for here lurk scorpions and vipers
if you only dare to look!

CAN YOU FIND these bold, bright creatures?

I may be the world's largest bird, but I can't fly, haven't you heard? I'm a... **NORTH AFRICAN OSTRICH**

I have one hump and two-toed feet, across the desert I walk in the heat. I'm a... **DROMEDARY CAMEL**

I like to graze on plants and leaves. My long neck can reach up with ease. I'm a... **GAZELLE**

A spotted cat, at speed I excel. My favourite prey? A shy gazelle! I'm a... **SAHARAN CHEETAH**

A long-tailed rodent, I jump so high. They can't catch me even if they try! I'm a... **JERBOA**

Snakes and birds can't eat me at all, when I roll into a spiky ball. I'm a... **DESERT HEDGEHOG**

NOW LOOK EVEN MORE CLOSELY
for these masters of disguise...

Large ears cool me
in this desert land,
a yellow coat shields
me in the sand.
I'm a... **FENNEC FOX**

Close to the ground
is where I dwell,
my spotted feathers
hide me well.
I'm a... **SPOTTED
SANDGROUSE**

Across the sand
I like to slither,
my horns and fangs
will make you shiver.
I'm a... **DESERT
HORNED VIPER**

A large lizard
with stripey scales,
I hunt mice and birds
and rarely fail.
I'm a... **DESERT
MONITOR**

By day I shelter
away from the sun,
from my deadly tail
you'd better run.
I'm a... **DEATH-
STALKER SCORPION**

I have long horns
shaped like spirals,
my white summer coat
is key to survival.
I'm an... **ADDAX
ANTELOPE**

Notes... on THE SAHARA DESERT

THE SAHARA DESERT COVERS MORE THAN 3 MILLION SQUARE MILES AND IS ONE OF THE SUNNIEST PLACES ON EARTH.

The long hours of sunshine mean the sand gets extremely hot during the day. Animals that live here have to be able to survive the intense heat and lack of water.

Many animals that call the Sahara Desert home have perfected the art of disguise.

DID YOU SPOT ALL OF THE MASTERS OF DISGUISE?

Turn back a page to see if you can find the creatures below, whose camouflage makes them nearly impossible to find.

Did you see my large, bat-like ears?

My ears help me to listen out for prey and predators!

Sandgrouse eggs are pale and spotted.

FENNEC FOX
Vulpes zerda

A fennec fox has two oversized ears, similar to those of a bat, which keep the animal cool in the daytime by giving off body heat. Thick fur helps it stay warm during the cold desert nights.

SPOTTED SANDGROUSE
Pterocles senegallus

Blending in with its surroundings, this bird's sand-coloured speckled feathers are a good match for the desert sand.

Two horns above my eyes protect them from the desert sand.

I have a large body and a long, powerful tail. Find me on a rock, near the ostriches.

DESERT HORNED VIPER
Cerastes cerastes

A horned viper spends the hot days buried in the sand or hiding under rocks. It comes out to hunt small mice and lizards at night.

DESERT MONITOR
Varanus griseus

Horizontal stripes on the monitor's tail help it to stay hidden.

Did you spot my long, curved horns?

Look out it under a bush, near the ostriches!

DEATHSTALKER SCORPION
Leiurus quinquestriatus

Deathstalker scorpions have eight legs and are part of the arachnid famlly, which includes spiders, mites and ticks.

ADDAX ANTELOPE
Addax nasomaculatus

Addax antelopes are rare. Their young, called calves, have sand-coloured coats. In summer, the addax's coat is more white-coloured or sandy-beige, but in winter it turns smoky grey.

Turn to page 43 to find all the animals in the Sahara

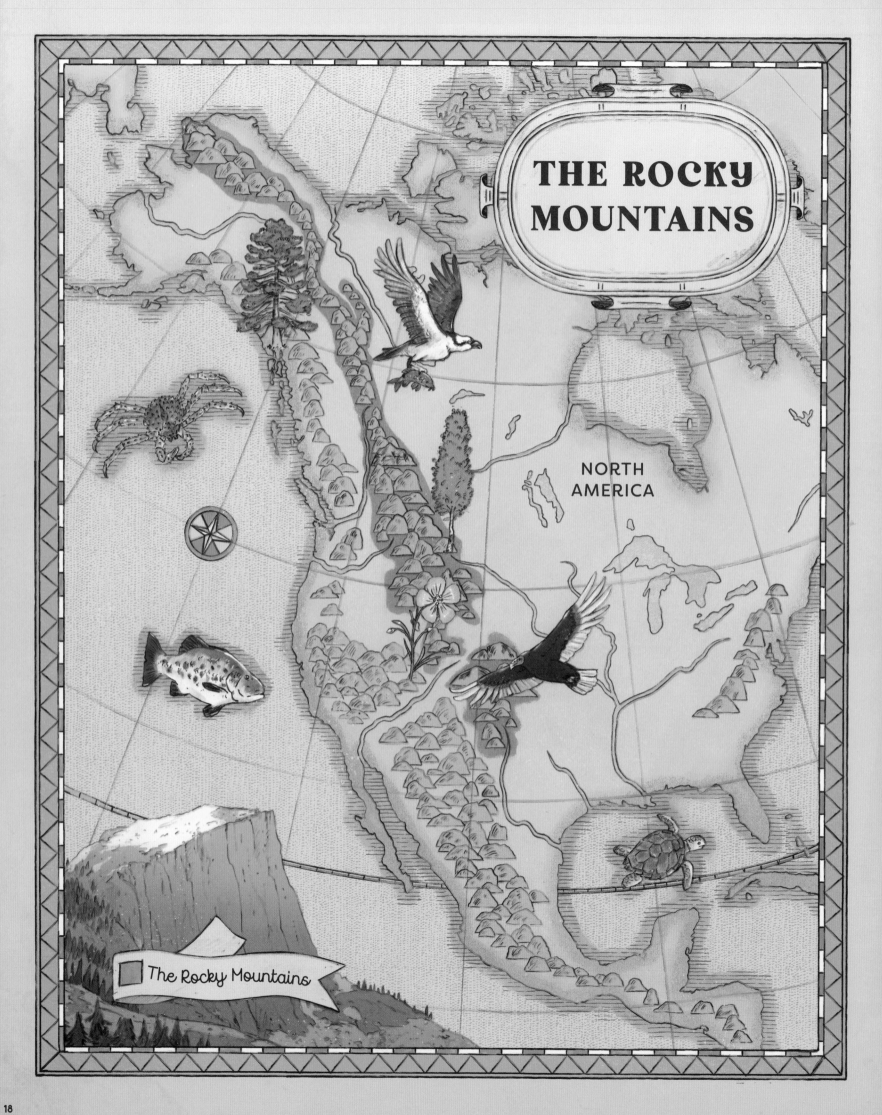

THE ROCKY MOUNTAINS

NORTH AMERICA

The Rocky Mountains

MOUNTAIN PUZZLE

Climb high upon these mountains;
explore their dizzy heights.
Find wildcats, birds and bighorn sheep,
and marvel at the sights.

Majestic creatures roam this land,
though some are hard to know,
like pygmy owls and bright-white hares
hiding in the snow.

CAN YOU FIND these bold, rugged creatures?

I'm the biggest cat out here... I stalk my prey, like elk and deer. I'm a... **MOUNTAIN LION**

Knocking on tree trunks I'll be found, listen out for my drumming sound. I'm an... **AMERICAN THREE–TOED WOODPECKER**

I nimbly cross the mountainside. My split hooves help me not to slide. I'm a... **BIGHORN SHEEP**

My patterned fur and my striped face give me camouflage in this place. I'm an... **AMERICAN BADGER**

My brilliant eyes and tufted ears help me to seek out snowshoe hares. I'm a... **CANADA LYNX**

My antlers grow to 4 feet tall (though females don't have them at all). I'm a... **ROCKY MOUNTAIN ELK**

NOW LOOK EVEN MORE CLOSELY *for these masters of disguise...*

My feathers make me
hard to follow...
Can you spot me
in a hollow?
I'm a... **NORTHERN
PYGMY OWL**

In autumn, my fur turns
from brown to white,
helping me to stay
out of sight.
I'm a... **SNOWSHOE HARE**

I'm a reptile —
winter's not my thing.
I burrow beneath the
ground, where I wait for
Spring! I'm a... **WESTERN
TIGER SALAMANDER**

With bright black eyes
and snow-white feathers,
I'm well disguised
in snowy weather.
I'm a... **WHITE-TAILED
PTARMIGAN**

I am an intrepid goat,
with horns, a beard
and a pure white coat.
I'm a... **ROCKY
MOUNTAIN GOAT**

Can you spot me
making a dam,
building up
a huge logjam?
I'm a... **BEAVER**

Notes on... THE ROCKY MOUNTAINS

THE ROCKY MOUNTAINS, ALSO KNOWN AS THE ROCKIES, STRETCH AROUND 3,000 MILES FROM BRITISH COLUMBIA IN WESTERN CANADA THROUGH TO NEW MEXICO IN THE UNITED STATES.

These jagged, snowy mountains may not look very hospitable, but they are an important habitat for hundreds of animals and contain a diverse range of wildlife.

DID YOU SPOT ALL OF THE MASTERS OF DISGUISE?

Turn back a page to see if you can find the creatures below, whose camouflage makes them nearly impossible to find.

NORTHERN PYGMY OWL
Glaucidium gnoma

The northern pygmy owl hunts for small mammals and insects during the day from its high perches in pine-forested mountains.

I'm so small you'll have to look carefully in the hollow of the pine tree!

You might just see me in the snow next to the small, yellow pine tree.

At the back of my head are large false eyes. This makes me look a lot bigger than I really am!

My large, furry feet help me move swiftly across the ice!

SNOWSHOE HARE
Lepus americanus

In winter, snowshoe hares have a snow-white winter coat to help them hide. In spring, the coat turns nut brown, so it's camouflaged once the ice has melted.

In spring, I stay close to my mate until she's ready to lay her eggs!

Here I am as a baby! After hatching, I have gills like a fish and live in water until I change into an adult!

WESTERN TIGER SALAMANDER
Ambystoma mavortium

Tiger salamanders breed in water. A female lays up to a hundred eggs, which hatch about four weeks later.

I use my summer and winter feathers to stay well hidden!

WHITE—TAILED PTARMIGAN
Lagopus leucura

Ptarmigans mostly eat buds, leaves and seeds. They prefer to walk, rather than fly, which explains why they rely so heavily on camouflage to survive.

Swimming close to the river's edge, I can be found busily building my lodge.

BEAVER
Castor canadensis

Beavers use their powerful jaw and strong teeth to cut down trees for branches to build their homes, which are known as lodges.

My hooves stop me from slipping on the ice... find me high up on the snowy slopes.

I have thick fur, rear webbed feet, and a flat tail for swimming!

ROCKY MOUNTAIN GOAT
Oreamnos americanus

Male goats are called billies and female goats are called nannies! Both billies and nannies have beards and horns!

Turn to page 44 to find all the animals in the Rocky Mountains

SOUTH
AMERICA

Amazon Basin

THE
AMAZON
BASIN

RAINFOREST PUZZLE

Pass beside the water,
where wild things walk —
find frogs, big cats and monkeys...
and birds that can talk!

Get lost within the canopy.
Scour the forest floor.
Solve this picture puzzle...
turn the page to find out more!

CAN YOU FIND these bold, bright creatures?

A big cat hidden
by rainforest trees,
I use my night vision
to hunt with ease.
I'm a... **JAGUAR**

Atop the water –
watch me flee,
escaping those who
want to eat me!
I'm a... **COMMON
BASILISK**

I'm 13 feet long
and I love to bite!
Who here is brave enough
to challenge me to fight?
I'm a... **BLACK
CAIMAN**

I swing up high
from tree to tree.
Jaguars and caimans
can't catch me!
I'm a... **SPIDER MONKEY**

Perched on a branch,
I sit quite still,
while eating with my
bright yellow bill.
I'm a... **TOCO TOUCAN**

A flutter here,
a flutter there —
my golden wings
are everywhere.
I'm a... **SWALLOWTAIL
BUTTERFLY**

NOW LOOK EVEN MORE CLOSELY *for these masters of disguise...*

I can hide myself from prying eyes with tree-green skin and clear underside. I'm a... **NORTHERN GLASS FROG**

See the feathery tree stump yonder - "is it a bird" I hear you wonder? I'm a... **POTOO BIRD**

I'm the tiniest monkey in these trees. I'm quick and agile – you won't catch me! I'm a... **PYGMY MARMOSET**

In the shallows, I sit and brood. Fish and birds are my favourite food. I'm a... **GREEN ANACONDA**

My long neck hides inside my shell. Beneath the leaves I like to dwell. I'm a... **MATA MATA TURTLE**

I'll tell you now – I'm in no hurry, green algae makes my coat so furry. I'm a... **HOFFMANN'S TWO-TOED SLOTH**

Notes on... THE AMAZON BASIN

LOCATED EAST OF THE ANDES MONTAINS, AND STRETCHING FROM THE GUIANA HIGHLANDS IN THE NORTH TO THE BRAZILIAN HIGHLANDS IN THE SOUTH, THE AMAZON BASIN IS THE LARGEST RIVER SYSTEM IN THE WORLD.

It is covered by the Amazon rainforest — one of the world's most important habitats — which is home to 40,000 species of plants, 1,300 of birds, 3,000 of fish, 430 of mammals, and 2.5 million species of insects. Many animals that call the river basin home camouflage themselves within its dense flora.

DID YOU SPOT ALL THE MASTERS OF DISGUISE?

Turn back a page to see if you can find the creatures below, whose camouflage makes them nearly impossible to find.

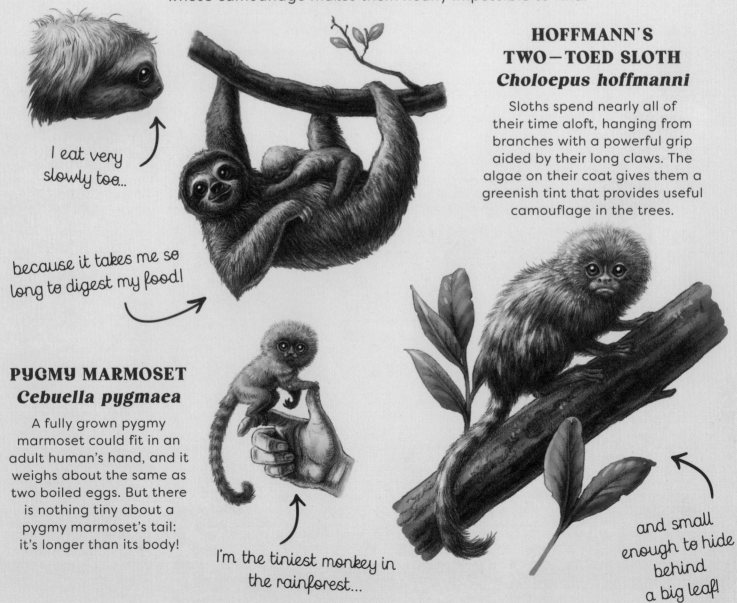

I eat very slowly too...

because it takes me so long to digest my food!

HOFFMANN'S TWO—TOED SLOTH
Choloepus hoffmanni

Sloths spend nearly all of their time aloft, hanging from branches with a powerful grip aided by their long claws. The algae on their coat gives them a greenish tint that provides useful camouflage in the trees.

PYGMY MARMOSET
Cebuella pygmaea

A fully grown pygmy marmoset could fit in an adult human's hand, and it weighs about the same as two boiled eggs. But there is nothing tiny about a pygmy marmoset's tail: it's longer than its body!

I'm the tiniest monkey in the rainforest...

and small enough to hide behind a big leaf!

I'm a bird... who looks a bit like a tree stump!

POTOO BIRD
Nyctibius griseus

This master of camouflage perches upright in the rainforest's canopy as it sleeps during the day, aligning its body to it to appear like an extension of a tree's branch.

MATA MATA TURTLE
Chelus fimbriata

Blending in with leaf litter on river bottoms, the mata mata is a poor swimmer but has adapted legs for walking on the bottom of its muddy habitat.

Find me under a pile of leaves - not far from a hungry caiman!

GREEN ANACONDA
Eunectes murinus

The spotting on the green anaconda helps it to blend into muddy waters. It can lie in wait for prey for hours while almost completely submerged and hidden from sight.

Look closely for my tiny green body. Did you find me perched on a lily pad?

NORTHERN GLASS FROG
Centrolenella fleischmanni

Just 2 — 3cm in length, this remarkable Amazonian frog has skin on its belly so translucent that you can see its beating heart and other organs!

Swimming in the shallows, I slither around the tree... hidden from the fish nearby.

Turn to page 45 to find all the animals in the Amazon

The Great Barrier Reef

AUSTRALIA

THE GREAT
BARRIER REEF

CORAL REEF PUZZLE

Deep beneath a sea of blue
the coral reef sings out,
calling us to look in awe...
at what it's all about!

Sharks, small fish and sea stars,
all call these waters home.
So dive into this puzzle —
Earth's rainbow-bright biome!

CAN YOU FIND these bold, bright creatures?

Know me by my
black-tipped fins,
as swiftly through
the reef I swim.
I'm a... **BLACKTIP
REEF SHARK**

Strong flippers and
a teardrop shell,
help me glide
and dive so well.
I'm a... **GREEN TURTLE**

Orange and white
stripes cover me
as I hide among
the anemone.
I'm a... **CLOWN FISH**

By thick, fleshy lips
my sharp teeth
are concealed,
sea urchins are
my favourite meal.
I'm a... **MAORI
WRASSE**

I graze on grass
beneath the sea,
my baby calf stays
close to me.
I'm a... **DUGONG**

I flit through the reef
like a butterfly.
My disk shape and
stripes will catch
your eye.
I'm a... **BUTTERFLY
FISH**

Blue spots are all
you'll see of me,
crabs and fish
they cannot flee.
I'm a... **BLUE-SPOTTED
RIBBONTAIL RAY**

A master of
disguise am I,
among the coral
is where I lie.
I'm a... **BROADCLUB
CUTTLEFISH**

I'm a flash of green
with orange dots,
branching corals
are my favourite spot.
I'm a... **LONGNOSE FILEFISH**

My giant shell
is spotted blue,
upon this reef
will I stay true.
I'm a... **GIANT CLAM**

Eight wriggly tentacles
give me away,
they help me snatch
and hold my prey.
I'm a...**WHITE-
STRIPED OCTOPUS**

A horse, as small as
a fingernail...
oddly, the one who gives
birth is male!
I'm a...

THE GREAT BARRIER REEF, OFF THE NORTHEAST COAST OF AUSTRALIA, IS MORE THAN 1,400 MILES LONG! IT'S THE WORLD'S LARGEST CORAL REEF.

It's home to 400 species of coral, which form the biggest collection in the world. There are also 1,500 different types of fish and 4,000 kinds of molluscs. It's an important habitat for rare species such as the dugong and the green turtle, which are threatened with extinction.

Many animals that live here have perfected the art of disguise, camouflaging themselves against the reef's bright colours.

DID YOU SPOT ALL THE MASTERS OF DISGUISE?

Turn back a page to see if you can find the creatures below, whose camouflage makes them nearly impossible to find.

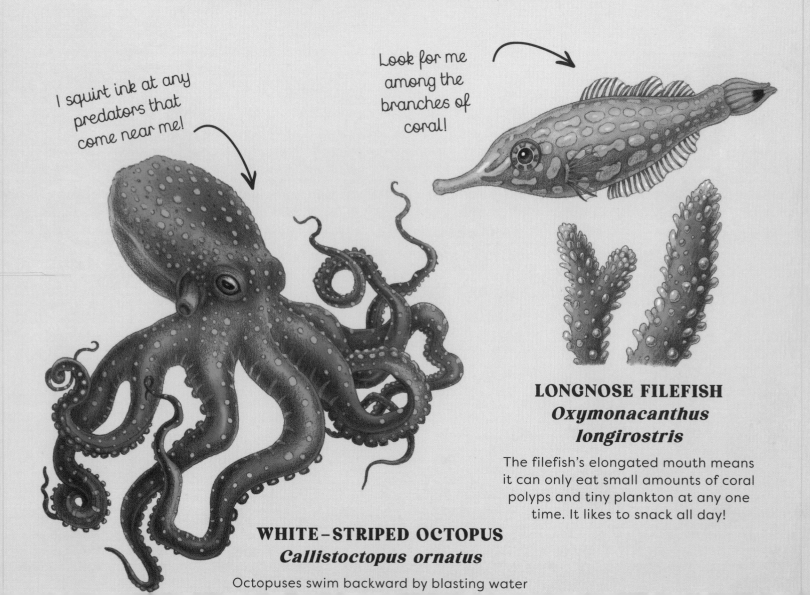

I squirt ink at any predators that come near me!

Look for me among the branches of coral!

LONGNOSE FILEFISH
Oxymonacanthus longirostris

The filefish's elongated mouth means it can only eat small amounts of coral polyps and tiny plankton at any one time. It likes to snack all day!

WHITE-STRIPED OCTOPUS
Callistoctopus ornatus

Octopuses swim backward by blasting water

Did you find me in the sand, near the dugong?

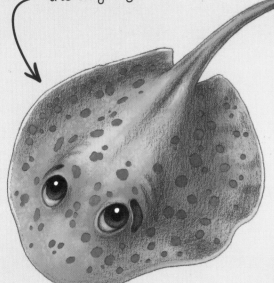

The nodules on my body exactly match my coral home...

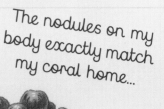

PYGMY SEAHORSE
Hippocampus bargibanti

The male pygmy seahorse can give birth to up to 34 baby seahorses at a time.

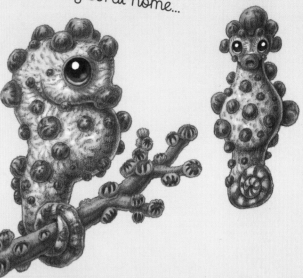

BLUE–SPOTTED RIBBONTAIL RAY
Taeniura lymma

At night, the ribbontail ray leaves its sandy hideaway to hunt. It scoops up its prey easily with its snout.

My flat body lets me stay hidden near the seabed...

BROADCLUB CUTTLEFISH
Sepia latimanus

This creature is a cunning predator that hypnotizes its prey with flashing, coloured bands that ripple along its skin.

My huge shell is so big, a child could curl up inside it!

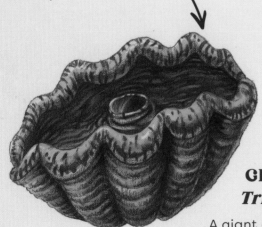

Giant clams can live up to 100 years!

GIANT CLAM
Tridacna gigas

A giant clam's bright colours are partly due to the algae living inside its body.

Turn to page 46 to find all the animals in the reef

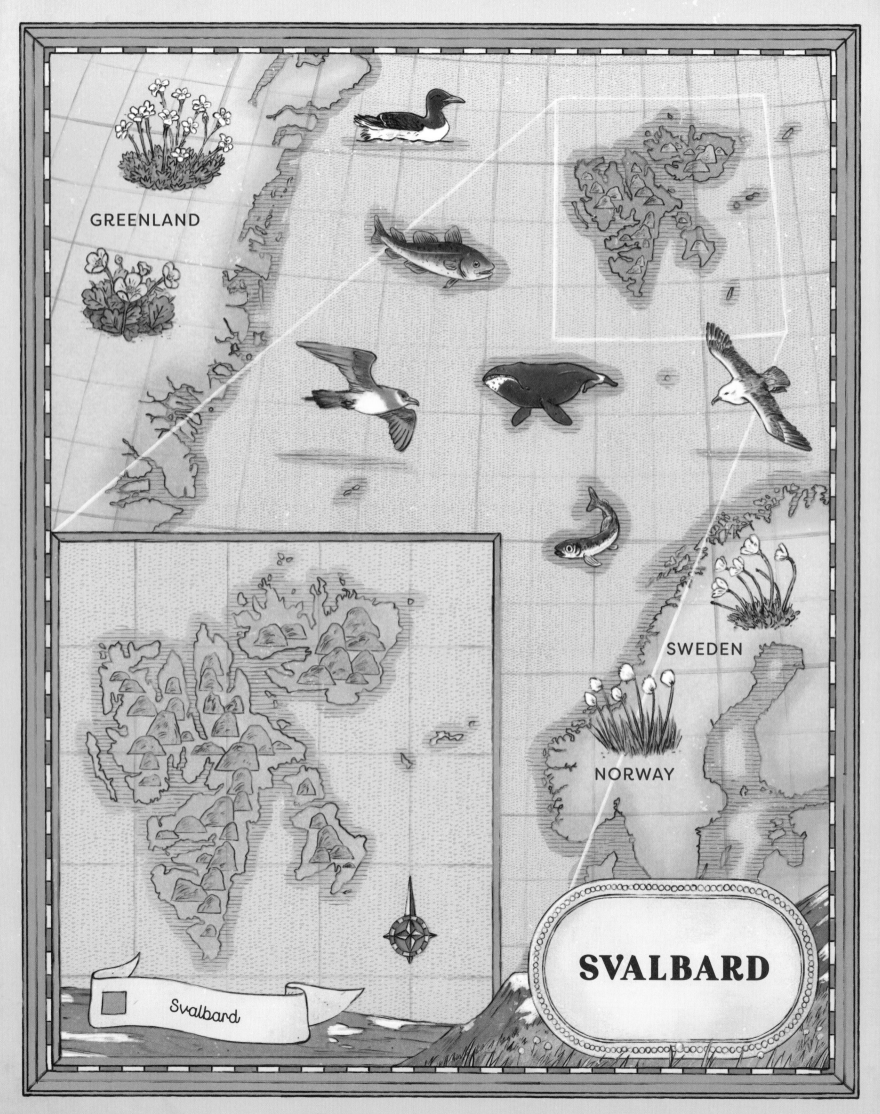

GREENLAND

SWEDEN

NORWAY

Svalbard

SVALBARD

ARCTIC PUZZLE

Rugged land of the midnight sun,
and frozen seas and tundra,
where reindeer, seals and walruses,
over icy ground do wander.

Can you spot the polar bear,
with fur so snowy white?
The Arctic fox and little auks
have vanished out of sight!

CAN YOU FIND
these bold, bright creatures?

My coat is warm and greyish brown.
Furry hooves stop me from falling down.
I'm a... **SVALBARD REINDEER**

My big flippers help me swim with ease,
I rise to the surface so I can breathe.
I'm a... **HUMPBACK WHALE**

Two tusks give me power during fights.
They also help me climb onto the ice.
I'm a... **WALRUS**

Swooping down, I dive quite deep,
catching fish in my colourful beak.
I'm an... **ATLANTIC PUFFIN**

My large, domed head might look quite odd.
I live in a family known as a pod.
I'm a... **BELUGA WHALE**

White spots and rings give me my name,
hiding from polar bears is my game.
I'm a... **RINGED SEAL**

NOW LOOK EVEN MORE CLOSELY
for these masters of disguise...

Bright white fur keeps
me hidden away.
Rabbits and birds
are my favourite prey.
I'm an... **ARCTIC FOX**

I've square flippers
and a bristly chin,
when I spot food
I dive right in.
I'm a... **BEARDED
SEAL**

Like a penguin,
I am black and white,
I flap my wings with
all my might.
I'm a... **LITTLE AUK**

Through icy cracks
I will appear.
My tusk is long,
just like a spear.
I'm a... **NARWHAL**

The Arctic fox is a
dangerous foe,
so I make my nest
in places it can't go.
I'm a... **SNOW
BUNTING**

I'm the biggest bear,
don't you know?
My white fur hides
me against the snow.
I'm a... **POLAR BEAR**

Notes on... SVALBARD

THE ISLANDS OF NORWAY'S SVALBARD ARE KNOWN FOR THEIR RUGGED, REMOTE TERRAIN OF GLACIERS, SEA ICE AND FROZEN TUNDRA. THE NORTHERN LIGHTS ARE VISIBLE DURING WINTER, WHILE SUMMER BRINGS THE MIDNIGHT SUN.

Majestic polar bears, whales and seals call this area home and have successfully adapted to its harsh environment.

DID YOU SPOT ALL OF THE MASTERS OF DISGUISE?

Turn back a page to see if you can find the creatures below, whose camouflage makes them nearly impossible to find.

My thick winter coat has dense underfur and long guard hairs to protect me from the cold. Look for me near the reindeer.

At night, I keep warm by wrapping my long, thick tail around me like a blanket.

I look a bit like a penguin, but I'm able to fly. See me perched on the rocks, near the walrus?

ARCTIC FOX
Vulpes lagopus

The Arctic fox is perfectly adapted to the harsh Arctic environment. It is a skilled hunter, catching geese, seabirds, and even seal pups. In summer, its fur changes to a greyish brown colour, which hides it in the changing landscape.

LITTLE AUK
Alle alle

In winter, little auks migrate, or travel, to warmer parts of the world such as the North Atlantic Ocean, and sometimes as far south as the United Kingdom.

My light-coloured feathers help me to blend in with the rocks and ice.

At nearly 2.5 metres long, I'm one of the largest seals in the Arctic.

BEARDED SEAL
Erignathus barbatus

Bearded seals are perfectly suited to life in the Arctic. Their streamlined bodies and powerful flippers make them excellent swimmers. A thick layer of fat, called blubber, helps to keep them warm.

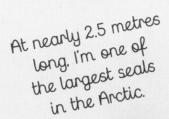

My tusk is a long, spiralled tooth!

SNOW BUNTING
Plectrophenax nivalis

The vegetation on the tundra grows low to the ground, so snow buntings need to stay hidden, otherwise they are easy prey for predators such as Arctic foxes.

I spend most of the time living below cracks in the dense pack ice. Look for me with my pod. on the water's surface.

POLAR BEAR
Ursus maritimus

The polar bear is an exceptional hunter with a keen sense of smell.. They can detect seals nearly 1.6 kilometres away.

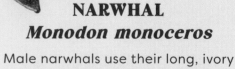

NARWHAL
Monodon monoceros

Male narwhals use their long, ivory tusks to show their strength and dominance over other males and to compete for females.

I am the largest bear in the world!

Turn to page 47 to find all the animals in the Arctic

FOREST PUZZLE Answers

1. KONIK PONY

2. FALLOW DEER

3. ADDER

4. BADGER

5. MIDDLE-SPOTTED WOODPECKER

6. WILD BOAR

7. WESTERN CAPERCAILLIE

8. EUROPEAN DORMOUSE

9. BROWN HARE

10. RED FOX

11. FIRE SALAMANDER

12. EAGLE OWL

DESERT PUZZLE Answers

1. NORTH AFRICAN OSTRICH
2. DROMEDARY CAMEL
3. GAZELLE
4. SAHARAN CHEETAH
5. JERBOA
6. DESERT HEDGEHOG
7. FENNEC FOX
8. SPOTTED SANDGROUSE
9. DESERT HORNED VIPER
10. DESERT MONITOR
11. DEATHSTALKER SCORPION
12. ADDAX ANTELOPE

MOUNTAIN PUZZLE Answers

1. MOUNTAIN LION

2. AMERICAN THREE-TOED WOODPECKER

3. BIGHORN SHEEP

4. AMERICAN BADGER

5. CANADA LYNX

6. ROCKY MOUNTAIN ELK

7. NORTHERN PYGMY OWL

8. SNOWSHOE HARE

9. WESTERN TIGER SALAMANDER

10. WHITE-TAILED PTARMIGAN

11. ROCKY MOUNTAIN GOAT

12. BEAVER

RAINFOREST PUZZLE Answers

1. JAGUAR
2. COMMON BASILISK
3. BLACK CAIMAN
4. SPIDER MONKEY
5. TOCO TOUCAN
6. SWALLOWTAIL BUTTERFLY
7. GLASS FROG
8. POTOO BIRD
9. PYGMY MARMOSET
10. GREEN ANACONDA
11. MATA MATA TURTLE
12. HOFFMANN'S TWO-TOED SLOTH

CORAL REEF PUZZLE Answers

1. BLACKTIP REEF SHARK
2. GREEN TURTLE
3. CLOWN FISH
4. MAORI WRASSE
5. DUGONG
6. BUTTERFLYFISH
7. BLUE-SPOTTED RIBBONTAIL RAY
8. BROADCLUB CUTTLEFISH
9. LONGNOSE FILEFISH
10. GIANT CLAM
11. WHITE-STRIPED OCTOPUS
12. PYGMY SEAHORSE

ARCTIC PUZZLE Answers

1. SVALBARD REINDEER
2. HUMPBACK WHALE
3. WALRUS
4. ATLANTIC PUFFIN

5. BELUGA WHALE
6. RINGED SEAL
7. ARCTIC FOX
8. BEARDED SEAL

9. LITTLE AUK
10. NARWHAL
11. SNOW BUNTING
12. POLAR BEAR

FURTHER READING

Illuminature
by Carnovsky

Animalium
by Jenny Broom
and Katie Scott

Animalia
by Graeme Base

Find out about Animal Camouflage
by Martin Jenkins

Animal Camouflage
by Sam Hutchison

How to talk to a tiger
by Jason Bittel and Kelsey Buzzell

5 Minute Nature Stories
by Gabby Dawnay and Mona K.

The Secret Signs of Nature
by Craig Caudill and Carrie Shryock

MAGIC CAT PUBLISHING

Picture Puzzler © 2023 Magic Cat Publishing Ltd
Text © 2023 Magic Cat Publishing
Illustrations © 2023 Ksenia Bakhareva
First Published in 2023 by Magic Cat Publishing Ltd
Unit 2 Empress Works, 24 Grove Passage, London E2 9FQ, UK

A catalogue record for this book is available from the British Library.

ISBN 978-1-913520-98-4

The illustrations were created in pencil and coloured digitally
Set in Hasthon, Filson Soft, HV Cocktail and Cursive Script Light

Published by Rachel Williams and Jenny Broom
Designed by Nicola Price and Sophie Gordon
Edited by Sam Williams and Helen Cumberbatch

Manufactured in China, TLF0523

9 8 7 6 5 4 3 2 1

FSC
www.fsc.org
MIX
Paper | Supporting responsible forestry
FSC® C104723